# MONSTER SCHOOL

## Colours, Shapes and Opposites

### EARLY LEARNING MADE FUN!

**Illustrated by**
SUE KING

**Written by**
ANDY CHARMAN

INDEX

First published in 1995 by Ultimate Editions

© 1995 Anness Publishing Limited

Ultimate Editions is an imprint of
Anness Publishing Limited
Boundary Row Studios
1 Boundary Row
London SE1 8HP

This edition distributed exclusively
in Canada by Book Express, an imprint of
Raincoast Books Distribution Limited

ISBN 1 86035 051 8

Editorial Director Joanna Lorenz
Editorial Consultant Jackie Fortey
Editor Belinda Wilkinson
Designed by Millions Design

PRINTED IN SINGAPORE

# CONTENTS

# COLOURS

# Monster <u>Red</u> is under the bed.

# Monster **<u>Blue</u>** has lost her shoe.

**Monster <u>Yellow</u> is feeling mellow.**

# Monster **<u>Green</u>** can hardly be seen.

# Monster <u>Black</u> lives in a shack.

# Monster <u>White</u> stays up all night.

# Monster **Purple** jumping the hurdle.

# Monster <u>Brown</u> playing the clown.

# Monster <u>Orange</u> likes things with a fringe.

# Monster **<u>Pink</u>** takes time to think.

# Monster <u>Grey</u> comes out to play.

# Monster <u>Mauve</u> finds shells in the cove.

# Monster <u>Turquoise</u> plays with her toys.

# Monster **Silver** is quick to deliver.

**Monster <u>Gold</u> is feeling bold.**

**But monsters made of many <u>colours</u> are even brighter than all the others.**

# SHAPES

# Building with <u>cubes</u> just for fun.

# Sailing <u>triangles</u> out in the sun.

# Baking a tasty <u>oval</u> pie.

# Flying <u>diamond</u> kites in the sky.

**Sending <u>hearts</u> to the one you love.**

**Gazing up at <u>stars</u> above.**

# Painting <u>blobs</u> upon the wall.

# Watching heavy <u>raindrops</u> fall.

# Sitting on a <u>semi-circle</u> in the park.

# Hiding from <u>zig-zags</u> in the dark.

# Putting <u>oblongs</u> just out of reach.

# Picking up <u>spiral</u> shells on the beach.

# Rolling <u>circles</u> with great glee.

It's a world of <u>shapes</u> for you and me.

# OPPOSITES

# You have to go <u>up</u>...

**to go <u>down</u>.**

# Monsters can feel <u>small</u>...
## and <u>large</u> at the same time.

# One monster's <u>hot</u>...

s another monster's <u>cold</u>.

# Inside every **<u>fat</u>** monster...

is a <u>thin</u> one
trying to get out.

If it's clean <u>inside</u>...

he monsters must be <u>outside</u>.

# When monsters are <u>sad</u>...

**ucks are happy.**

# Let the monster <u>sleep</u>...

**or it will keep you <u>awake</u>.**

# If the monster is <u>full</u>...

# the cupboard must be <u>empty</u>.

# Monsters who go <u>fast</u>...

sometimes have to go <u>slow</u>.

# Young monsters...

**always learn from the <u>old</u>.**

# but you can't make him <u>stop</u>.

# A monster going out...

...an meet a monster coming in.

# Monsters can be straight...

**but most of them are <u>curly</u>.**

# It's always the <u>dry</u> monsters...

who make you the most <u>wet</u>.

When a big monster whispers...

t sounds
ike a **<u>shout</u>**.

**Every monster one day meets his <u>opposite</u>.**